This is the Blackbird

who sings
for
Caroline

With all good wishes

John Mole
Mary Norman

Illustrated by Mary Norman

JOHN MOLE

This is the Blackbird

PETERLOO POETS

First published in 2007
by Peterloo Poets
The Old Chapel, Sand Lane, Calstock,
Cornwall PL18 9QX, U.K.

**A catalogue record for this book is available
from the British Library**

ISBN 9781904324447

Printed by 4word Ltd,
Unit15, Baker's Park, Cater Road, Bristol BS13 7TT

ACKNOWLEDGEMENTS

This volume is a selection of poems written since the publication of my two Peterloo volumes, *Boo to a Goose* and *The Mad Parrot's Countdown*, and designed as complementary to its predecessors. It contains poems from five collections published by Blackie, Hodder Children's Books, and Oxford University Press along with a number of new poems, several of which have appeared in various anthologies.

Supported by
The National Lottery®
through Arts Council England

for Anna and Benjamin

CONTENTS

9 First Impressions
10 Variation on an Old Rhyme
12 The Shoes
14 Riddles
16 Working in Winter
17 Instructions for Catching the Spider
18 The Song-Birds
20 The Lost Ball
21 Paradise
22 Everybody
23 The Maker
24 A Change of Scene
25 Four Things to Remember when Writing a Poem
26 The Hiding Place
28 The Balloon
29 First Love
31 The Jigsaw Man
32 Mr. Punch
34 Words
35 The Coastguard
36 Miss Lowman-Lang
38 The Coleridge Show
40 Gliders
41 Gnomic
42 A Lesson Taught by Kites
44 This is the Week
45 The Song of Abner Brown
50 She Heard Them Shouting
51 The Invisible Man
53 At the Swimming Pool
54 I Spy
55 The Bull
57 The Doctor and the Clown
59 Friends Again
61 At the Pantomime

62 The Unsuccessful Conjuror
64 Cuckoo Jones
65 A Call to Arms
66 Wordsworth's Watering Can
67 The Sad Story of Terrible Trevor
70 Once in a Dream
72 Potatoes
74 Wellington Boots
75 Nothing on Earth
76 Song of the Lonely Monster
77 At the House of Superstition
78 First Day
80 Finding the Magic
81 Another Day on the Beach
83 Fair Exchange
84 Who Goes There?
85 A Prize Exhibit
86 Glove on a Spiked Railing
87 Pet Sounds
88 The Inner Dog
89 European Eagle Owl at The World Owl Trust
90 Learning to be a Ghost
92 There Was a Time
93 Songs for Seven Storeys
93   PROLOGUE
94   OCEAN
95   ARCTIC
96   FOREST
96   BEACH
97   SAVANAH
98   MOUNTAINS
99   EPILOGUE (SKY)

First Impressions

Put them down quickly however they come
in whatever order, let them go where they will
like laying the table in a rush.
This is a meal for one though we're all hungry.
Where are your manners? Forget them.
Think about holding back a little later
when you're making the arrangements
and the spread is there. Perhaps then
the refinement of a paper napkin
or a place-name for your teacher, but for now
the improvised solo banquet, the acceptable
measure of your greed, wolfing each syllable
as a taster, licking your fingers
as the words arrive. Go on, indulge yourself
before you send the invitations,
grab and mix for the sheer confectionary
thrill of it, the savoury, the sweet,
the raw, the cooked, the wonder-dish
served up by language for a gathering
you'll soon become the host of. Put them
all down, all the sounds, the colours,
as they come, a bumper feast in readiness
and only one word for the sum of it: Enjoy.

Variation on an Old Rhyme

This is the blackbird that wakes with a song.

This is the sun
That shines for the blackbird that wakes with a song.

This is the earth
That welcomes the sun
That shines for the blackbird that wakes with a song.

This is the snow that fell through the night
That covers the earth
That welcomes the sun
That shines for the blackbird that wakes with a song.

These are the children that cry with delight
That play in the snow that fell through the night
That covers the earth
That welcomes the sun
That shines for the blackbird that wakes with a song.

This is the wonderland of white
That surrounds the children that cry with delight
That play in the snow that fell through the night
That covers the earth
That welcomes the sun
That shines for the blackbird that wakes with a song.

This is the quarrel that started the fight
That stains the wonderland of white
That surrounds the children that cry with delight
That play in the snow that fell through the night
That covers the earth
That welcomes the sun
That shines for the blackbird that wakes with a song.

This is the wrong that none can put right
That caused the quarrel that started the fight
That stains the wonderland of white
That surrounds the children that cry with delight
That play in the snow that fell through the night
That covers the earth
That welcomes the sun
That shines for the blackbird that wakes with a song.

These are the nations in all their might
That suffer the wrong that none can put right
That caused the quarrel that started the fight
That stains the wonderland of white
That surrounds the children that cry with delight
That play in the snow that fell through the night
That covers the earth
That welcomes the sun
That shines for the blackbird that wakes with a song.

And this is the song that goes on in spite
Of all the nations in all their might
That suffer the wrong that none can put right
That causes the quarrels that start every fight
That stains the wonderland of white
That surrounds the children that cry with delight
That play in the snow that fell through the night
That covers the earth
That welcomes the sun
That shines just the same on everyone.

The Shoes

These are the shoes
Dad walked about in
When we did jobs
In the garden,
When his shed
Was full of shavings,
When he tried
To put the fence up,
When my old bike
Needed mending,
When the car
Could not get started,
When he got up late
On Sunday.
These are the shoes
Dad walked about in
And I've kept them
in my room.

These are not the shoes
That Dad walked out in
When we didn't know
Where he was going,
When I tried to lift
His suitcase,
When he said goodbye
And kissed me,
When he left his door-key
On the table,
When he promised Mum
He'd send a postcard,
When I couldn't hear
His special footsteps.
These are not the shoes
That Dad walked out in

But he'll need them
When he comes back home.

Riddles

You should be glad that through the dark
I kept awake; instead
With something like a grunt or bark
You bash me on the head;

Which only goes to show, I'd say,
As sure as I'm wound tight,
That people often break by day
The vows they made last night.

*

Whenever your meat's tough we tear it,
Whenever you're silent we're dumb,
And if we're a long pointed pair it
Could be that Dracula's come.

Whenever you grin we must bear it,
Whenever you're downcast we're glum,
And if you've a brace we must wear it;
We're a mouthful to live with, by gum!

*

Post-haste or slow,
Let there be no doubt
That wherever you go
I shall find you out
At whatever address,
And I mean business.

I'm dull, brown,
And I come at a price;
I watch you frown
With fear or surprise

At a name you know
Through my little window.

To send me again
Don't tear, use a knife
And a different name –
Ah well, it's a life!
Back and forth, back and forth
All over the earth.

*

We sparkle when you smile,
We wobble when you cough,
Sometimes a metre seems a mile
When you take us off.

In rain or sunny weather
When you're tired we're there
To hold your world together.
A very helpful pair.

If you do not need us
We're cushioned in a case
Until your fate has freed us
To perch upon your face.

Spectacles
Envelope
Teeth
Alarm clock

Working in Winter

Silently the snow settles on the scaffolding,
The feathery flakes furry and flick their fragments,
The brown bricks piled on billowing polythene
Heap their heaviness to heavenly heights.
Workmen in woolly hats whistle into the wind
Or dance in donkey jackets to hold in heat,
Their toes tingle, the tips of their fingers freeze –
It's murder, mate, this job is, murder.
Roll on five o'clock!

Instructions for Catching the Spider

1

Slip it between an upturned cup
Or tumbler and a postcard
Carefully slid in under it, remembering
That just because it doesn't buzz
You can't assume
It likes the darkness.

2

Walk to the door
Or nearest window if it opens easily,
Slide back the postcard, let
The light in, gently tip the cup
Or tumbler, wait
Until the spider's ready.

3

Watch it hang a moment
In a web of air
As if somehow attached to it
Before it drifts down, landing
Right-way-up because its legs are everywhere,
And scampers off across the garden.

The Song-Birds

When William Wordsworth heard the news
Just one thing caused him sorrow.
He didn't have a smart dress-suit
So a suit he had to borrow.

His fame had led Her Majesty
To make him Poet Laureate
"But I haven't got a smart dress-suit"
He cried, "Who has one? May I borrow it?"

"Of course." said Samuel Rogers who
Was a full six inches smaller
(Samuel was a poet too
But William was taller).

So he squeezed into that suit
And paid the Queen his visit
And she was too polite to say
"That isn't *your* suit, is it!"

A song-bird in a borrowed suit –
Could any sight be sorrier?
But Wordsworth was a famous man
And she was Queen Victoria.

When Wordsworth died, Lord Tennyson
Took over as PL
And at his own investiture
Wore Samuel's suit as well.

He wore it as a tribute to
That late great Man of Letters
But as he wasn't quite so tall
It fitted him much better.

So when her proud new Laureate
Walked through the Royal door
The Queen was too polite to say
"I've seen that suit before!"

When Tennyson died, the next PL
Was a man called Alfred Austin.
He wore his own suit on the day
Though we don't know what it cost him.

We don't know, either, much about
His verse. It's been forgotten.
No doubt the Queen thought it was good
But some say it was rotten.

The Lost Ball

Flying up against the sun
The ball goes, and you try
To follow it until the dazzle
Blacks it out, and in the darkness
Someone calls "Your turn
To fetch it!" and you run
Through gradual light
To where you think it went
But when you turn again to check
The angle that it came from
All you find is emptiness
And silence where your friends were
Who have upped and gone
Or were they ever there, you wonder,
As the sun goes in
And who is this you
Thought was you who
Scrabbles among earth, long grass
And brambles, looking for a ball
Which maybe no one ever threw
And never landed?

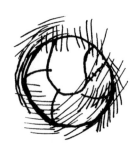

Paradise

Climbing up into my father's
Barrow of cut grass
And sinking gently, all that
Thick warm moisture
Moulded round me, then
The mower's hum becoming louder,
Nearer, stuttering to a halt
And Dad pretending not to know
I'm in there, shaking out
Another load of luscious
Freshness onto me and muttering
I wonder where he is?
And me about to answer
Here I am but then
Deciding not to.

Everybody

She's good at everything
And everybody says she is.

I'm good for nothing
And you keep on telling me.

I wish you'd sometimes say
I'm good at something.

It's not my fault I don't like
Anything she's good at.

Why do you keep on telling me
What everybody says?

Who is everybody anyway?
It's all your fault.

The Maker

They say the sun,
The moon, the stars,
Bow down to him, this
Brilliant quick-fingered
Bringer of light
To gold and silver leaf,

Yet all he knows
Is only how much more
There's left to know, how
Every maker, even he,
Is merely love's apprentice
In the studio of dreams.

A Change Of Scene

I couldn't stay, I couldn't go.
What was it there that held me so
Between the darkness and the light?
Two ghosts who would not leave my sight.

They seemed a mother and her child
Picnicking in a golden field
And not a cloud was in the sky
And nobody was asking why.

I couldn't sleep, I couldn't wake.
It felt as if a storm might break
But not on them, not there, oh no
Not on that scene which held me so

Until it changed, when suddenly
Those ghosts took one last look at me,
The field grew dark, the golden land
Was nothing but a waste of sand.

Nothing but dust stretched on and on,
The mother and her child had gone
And in their place no picnicking
But hunger vaguely wandering,

Millions of mothers crouching there.
Millions of children eating air.
I couldn't go, I had to stay.
It's only dreams that go away

And this was not a dream, I knew.
The day had come, the night was through
And everyone was asking why,
And so was I. And so was I.

Four Things To Remember When Writing A Poem

A watched pot
Never boils.

A watched phone
Never rings.

A watched clock
Never strikes.

A watched song
Never sings.

The Hiding Place

No, I shall never tell you
Where it is or even
Why I haven't told you
Yet, but if you must
Keep searching, watch
For where my footprints
Disappear, be ready
For a hand which isn't mine
To touch your shoulder, listen
For your own voice echoing
Where are you? Then prepare
For no surprises, only
What I could have told you
Long before you set out
For the hiding place,
That if you ever find it
I shall not be there.

The Balloon

It's all hot air they said
You'll never do it
But now the laugh's on them
As up and up I go
Beyond their ordinary world.

I look down, sorry
For the tilted faces
And those tiny handkerchiefs
Which wave together,
Proud of me at last.

Wherever I land
Will be different.
I shall step out
A qualified dreamer
With his feet on the ground.

First Love

Everyone says that my girlfriend Gemma
Is big for her age
And that what we apparently feel for each other
Is only a stage.

But what, when they grumble, I have to agree
Is as plain as day
Is that Gemma tends to throw her big weight about
Every which way.

Once when I showed her a shed in our garden
She climbed on the roof
And then when I wasn't expecting leapt down
                              like an Amazon.
Strewth!

All of my breath was completely knocked out of me,
All of my puff,
But just to have Gemma landing on top of me
Was enough.

The Jigsaw Man

Do you really think you can
Keep up with the Jigsaw Man
Who sits and thinks and thinks and sits
Surrounded by a sea of bits
Of every shape, of every size,
Then suddenly, with blazing eyes,
Puts this one here and that one there
Yet still, it seems, finds time to spare
To smile at you, to watch your face
As he snaps them into place?
Ah yes, indeed, it may have been
Your idea to challenge him
But he belongs to those who know
Exactly where the pieces go.
A patch of land, a slice of sky,
A tree, a river running by,
The usual scene that you'd expect
With everything present and correct
So why, you wonder, couldn't you
Do what the Jigsaw Man can do
And fit it all inside its frame
Instead of merely feeling shame
When after thinking hard and long
You try a piece and find it's wrong,
Putting land where sky should be.
Oh better leave it all to me
He says, and then the puzzle's done.
The Jigsaw Man has upped and gone
Knowing that now you'll never know
Exactly where the pieces go
And leaving you the dullest bit,
The trouble of undoing it.

Mr. Punch

Did he have friends
When he was a kid?
Oh no he didn't.
Oh yes he did.

Was he ever upset
When his mum got so cross?
Oh no he wasn't.
Oh yes he was.

Had he frightened his sister
And laughed at his dad?
Oh no he hadn't.
Oh yes he had.

Should he learn manners
And try to be good?
Oh no he shouldn't.
Oh yes he should.

Does he go calling
Policemen "The Fuzz"?
Oh no he doesn't.
Oh yes he does.

When he is told to
Will he sit still?
Oh no he won't.
Oh yes he will.

Has he made up with Judy
Or turned down his jazz?
Oh no he hasn't.
Oh yes he has.

If he tried to explain
Would he be understood?
Oh no he wouldn't.
Oh yes he would.

Or must he stay always
A man we can't trust?
Oh no he mustn't.
Oh yes he must.

Words

come out
like stars sometimes
and choose the darkest nights
to sparkle in,

are gentle
water-drops suggesting
streams you cannot find the source of
in a landscape where no
water is,

or wasps
behind your back which
suddenly
go silent.

The Coastguard

Sometimes he asks the waves
as they recur
if there is nothing more
than this, the flat
shine of what is left
by their receding
then the roar
of their return, a come-
back leap
spray-dazzling
on the rocks
to yet another burst
of brief applause.

Their only answer
is the blown fringe
of a frothy curtain
tasselling the shore-line,
and a solitary
gull which struts
across the stage
of its reflection
lifting now one foot
and now the other

Miss Lowman-Lang

I sat at my desk with a china inkwell
sunk into its hole at the end of the runnel
you picked your pen up from, a twig-thin
wooden shaft with the nib stuck in
like a pigmy's weapon. It was good
for a stab and flick if you were in the mood
and your neighbour wasn't. Then
it was always time for *Settle Down!*
The ink we used was made from a powder
you could thicken into jelly. Our teacher
was Miss Lowman-Lang. She taught us writing,
to use those primitive pens without blotting,
to give each letter's backbone a loop
in the right place so that it linked up
into a chain called word which at our age
had little for us to do with language
but a lot with good behaviour.
I was eight (and two plus two was four).
She showed us with her special pen.
Its lever squeezed a tube inside. *Fountain*
she called it, and it used a special ink
from her bottle with a label: *Parker Quink.*
One day, when I was standing at her desk,
I plucked the courage up to ask
if I could hold it. *Yes of course,* she said
but do be careful. Then what I did
was take it (carefully) by the top bit
with the clip on and, oh no, the writing part
fell out and arrowed to the floorboards
where its gold nib stuck and quivered.
Everyone saw. Miss Lowman-Lang was kind,
although she couldn't say she didn't mind,
but I was dumbstruck. I could see
the nib was split apart and bent impossibly
beyond repair. I can still hear my fumbled

muttering of guilt *I'll take it home to Dad.*
My Dad'll know, my Dad'll mend it.
But, of course, he couldn't and I didn't,
nor was I old enough to say or even think
I'll pay for it although in time's indelible ink
and after fifty years of unforgotten shame
perhaps I'm paying as I write your name,
Miss Lowman-Lang, in joined-up writing.
This poem is for you, Miss Lowman-Lang.

The Coleridge Show

Samuel Taylor Coleridge's
Head was full of notions,
Of scholarship, philosophy
And passionate emotions.

Once he was away, it was
Impossible to stop him.
He'd talk and talk and talk and talk,
For talk you couldn't top him.

In fact, it really must be said
If you saw Samuel coming
Then that was probably the time
To turn round and start running.

His friend Charles Lamb, though, didn't
When they met on Hampstead Heath.
Once Samuel got started
He never paused for breath.

Lamb couldn't get a word in
However hard he tried.
Oh the breadth of Samuel's knowledge
Was infinitely wide.

On and on and on he went
This, that, and so-and-so,
While Lamb stood rooted to the spot
This was The Coleridge Show.

He listened and he listened,
For punishment a glutton
Then Samuel to stress a point
Tugged at Lamb's waistcoat button.

Off it came, and off went Lamb
Released for his walk at last
But according to one observer
Who later happened past

He saw a fellow, clearly mad,
(So he didn't choose to linger)
Lecturing to a tiny spot
Between his thumb and finger.

Gliders

Hoist them up, let go
The rope, just so
They hang there
Balancing on air.

The Sunday sky
Is suddenly
Full of them, their slim
Bodies, delicate and trim.

Such an intense,
Mysterious silence,
Such a slow, weightless,
Gradual progress.

Almost they repose
Above their own shadows,
Almost they keep
Watch over their own sleep,

Until with a sudden
Wakeful dipping down
They seem
As if snatched from a dream

To obey once more
The weekday law
Of nose to the ground,
Deadweight, earthbound.

Gnomic

I am the oldest known gnome,
No gnome is older than me,
I am the oldest known gnome
Though an unknown gnome there may be.

An unknown gnome there may be
But nobody knows of him yet
Therefore no gnome is older than me
So give me a little respect.

A Lesson Taught by Kites

Here on The Downs, our bright two-handers
Zap and clatter, criss-cross, frenzied
In a wind that whips them and knows
Nothing of control. Like scimitars
They slash across each other's flight paths
In a sudden execution of the air, or fall
As if betrayed by their own gaudiness,
A pride of emperors unseated, now again
Ascendant, tugged and lifted for another
Aerial enthronement, splendour
High above the grass, then once more
Dumped down by the wheel of fortune
In their slackened strings, no permanence
For even the most gorgeous, buoyant,
Effortless display. There's nothing we can do
But hold on tight, lean back, pay court
To triumph while it lasts, a flock of little people
Buffeted and scattered on these slopes
As fragments of the world around us
Teach the law that even beauty must obey.

This Is The Week

This is the week when you can hear a pin drop
but mustn't pick it up, when all the facts
stand to attention and you gaze in panic
at their unfamiliar faces. This is the week
when everyone seems to write faster
than you do and asks for more paper, when
the back of your friend's head is giving
nothing away that is any use. This
is the week of the surreptitious cough,
the pen that runs out, the staggered
dash to the toilet, the watched clock's
ruthless handiwork. This is the week
of the swot's apotheosis, the rebel's
bottoming-out, the cheat's come-uppance
and the teachers' unreadable minds
as their eyes meet yours. Then this
is the term that is almost over
except for the lists, the tall form order,
the praise, the blame, the could-do-better
which nevertheless are of less account
than a life to be lived and summer waiting.

The Song Of Abner Brown

This is Abner Brown,
My cat.

He *looks* lazy.
He *looks* fat.

He's good at making
Grumpy faces.

He likes to curl up
In shady places.

When strangers pass
He hears them say:

There lies a cat
Of yesterday!

And then he smiles
Because he knows

That there's more to him
Than they suppose.

Although he's many
Cat-years old,

Abner's a cat
Who is UNCONTROLLED.

He *may* look fat,
He *may* look lazy

But Abner's good
At going crazy.

He'll let you think
That he's asleep

Then suddenly
He'll make a leap.

Abner becomes
A ball of fur,

A bouncing bomb,
A flying purr.

Before you know it
Already he

Will have reached the top
Of the tallest tree.

He stretches, grins
And thumps his chest.

He thinks he's Tarzan
(Aren't you impressed?).

From branch to branch
He sways and swings

And this is the Abner
Song he sings;

Oh I am a cat
That gets around,

Just try to keep me
On the ground.

I may be old
And dim of eye

But Abner Brown
Was born to fly.

A scaredy cat?
Not me. No chance.

Watch this moggy
Skip and dance.

Tickle my ears
And shake my paw, sir!

Give me my milk
From a flying saucer.

Yesterday's cat
Was born to sorrow

But Abner's a cat
Of today and tomorrow.

Yesterday's cat?
Oh no, no, no.

Abner's a cat
On the go, go, go!

Then he gives his chest
One final thump

And you'd think for a moment
That he's going to jump,

But then my veteran
Abner Brown

Very gingerly
Scrambles down.

For every old cat
However tough

There comes a time
When he's had enough,

When it's wiser perhaps
To admit you're old

Than to go on being
Uncontrolled.

So back he limps
To his shady place

And the grumpy look
Returns to his face,

But he knows that I know
That before too long

He'll be up again
And singing his song.

She Heard Them Shouting

She heard them shouting at each other
Through her bedroom wall
But that was how it often was,
Nothing unusual.

She could never make out their words
Or begin to guess
Exactly what it was this time
Might have started the mess.

Once she lay awake
The whole night through,
Wondering what if anything
She could do.

Were they asleep yet,
Would it start again,
Would it be even louder
Or just the same?

She'd heard them shouting at each other
Through her bedroom wall
And now this silent waiting
Was worst of all.

The Invisible Man

The invisible man is a joker
Who wears an invisible grin
And the usual kind of visible clothes
Which cover up most of him,

But there's nothing above his collar
Or at the end of his sleeves,
And his laughter is like the invisible wind
Which rustles the visible leaves.

When the visible storm clouds gather
He strides through the visible rain
In a special invisible see-through cloak
Then invisibly back again.

But he wears a thick, visible overcoat
To go out when it visibly snows
And the usual visible footprints
Get left wherever he goes.

In the visible heat-haze of summer
And the glare of the visible sun,
He undoes his visible buttons
With invisible fingers and thumb,

Takes off his visible jacket,
Loosens his visible tie,
Then snaps his visible braces
As he winks an invisible eye.

Last thing in his visible nightgown
Tucked up in his visible bed
He rests on a visible pillow
His weary invisible head

And ponders by visible moonlight
What invisibility means
Then drifts into silent invisible sleep
Full of wonderful visible dreams.

At The Swimming Pool

Such a foot-slap hall of echoes
bouncing off each other
wall-to-white-tiled wall
across the water, meeting
midway as a hydra-headed
body of pure scream, falsetto,
fit to raise the roof
and cry blue murder.

Such a palace of parabola
and belly-flop, the perfect
cleaving plunge, the dead-weight
ignominious tumble's
loss of balance, such a field
of folk afloat, a spray-blessed
bobbing, winged and ringed
and skull-capped holiday.

But such, for some, a mayhem
of distraction, these the serious ones,
the steady back-and forthers
measuring their lengths, intent
on nothing but the next
completed turn, the adding up
to yet another more than yesterday
and with a privacy of purpose all their own.

I Spy

My black gloves are shiny,
My glasses are dark,
I wait on a bench
By a lake in the park.

My face is a blank
As the world passes by
Which is one of the things
About being a spy.

What I've learned to be good at
Is just sitting tight
With occasional glances
To left and to right

Then getting up slowly
And creeping along
At a pre-arranged time
To the next bench on

Where my sinister contact,
Another blank face,
Seems dead to the world
As he stares into space.

His black gloves are shiny,
His glasses are dark,
So we sit side by side
By a lake in the park.

The Bull

(in memory of Ted Hughes)

Look where he stands
alone in the meadow
with a brow of thunder
and a ring through his nose.

Like a heavy-weight boxer
he paws at the ground
and his dangerous eyes
say *Beware! Beware!*

He could send you sky-high
with a toss of his head.
His moon-slice horns
are a Viking's helmet.

But now look again
and his strength is gentle,
at rest in the cloud
of his steaming breath.

His rough tongue licks
at his grassy muzzle
and his tail frisks nimbly
this way and that.

Oh keep this creature
far from the ring,
from the cheering crowds
from the blood-stained sand.

May he live here in peace,
a king among cattle,
an earth-bound god
worth his weight in gold.

Thinking of You

Sometimes I think of you
the way that the thinnest
wisp of a cloud
teased out
to gauzy mist
drifts off across the blue,

but sometimes too
the dark sky loaded with thunder
presses down
like a slab of stone
which I lie under
thinking of you.

The Doctor and The Clown

A sad man went to the doctor
Who took one look and guessed
That his visitor wasn't physically ill
But was certainly depressed.

"You're right, so right," said the sad man,
"And I doubt if there's any cure
But I thought I should come to see you
Just to make doubly sure."

"I'm glad that you did," said the doctor
With a great big smile on his face,
"Because, as it just so happens,
You've come to the right place.

I'm not going to give you a tonic,
I'm not going to give you a pill,
But I am going to give you a word of advice
And take it if you will.

Last night I went to the circus
Which has just arrived in town
With a whole array of wonderful acts
But the best of them all is the clown.

Grock is his name, and believe me
He's really a clown and a half,
He'll double you up in stitches
And remind you how to laugh.

I can guarantee when you see him
Your troubles will melt away,
So book yourself a ringside seat
At once, without delay."

The sad man thanked him, turned to go
And shuffled towards the door
While the doctor noticed that he looked
Even sadder than before.

"Take my word for it," said the doctor,
"At least give the clown a chance."
The sad man summoned a rueful smile
And looked at him askance.

Then it suddenly occurred to the doctor
To ask the patient's name
"I know all about your problem
And the reason why you came

But who exactly are you?"
The sad man bowed his head.
"Haven't you guessed already?
I *am* Grock," he said.

Friends Again?

When snow melts to slush
And noise becomes hush,
When smile answers frown
And upside turns down,
When bitter tastes sweet
And both our ends meet
Then a flash in the pan
Will be what we began.

When each finds the other
And lose is discover,
When feeble feels strong
And short stretches to long,
When head rules the heart
And we make a fresh start,
Then if No or if Yes
Will be anyone's guess.

At The Pantomime

Yes, it was great to laugh
When one of the ugly sisters thought she was more beautiful
Than her other half,
And it was fun to cheer
When out of the magic lantern with a puff of smoke
We saw the genie appear,
And it was time to weep
When Snow White bit into the shiny apple
Or Beauty pricked her finger and fell asleep,
And it was really good
When the Prince arrived to wake them up
Though of course we knew that he would,
But best of all
When the villain sneaked on
(And, no, we didn't really want him to be gone)
It was absolute bliss
To hiss!

The Unsuccessful Conjuror

Whenever I'm stuck
and my tricks go wrong
someone in the audience
starts this song:

abracadabra,
just like that,
you've got no rabbit
and you've lost your hat.

When my face cracks up
with its silly grin,
they know the words
so they all join in:

abracadabra,
just like that,
you've got no rabbit
and you've lost your hat.

When the curtain falls
at the end of the show
I can hear them shouting
as I pack up to go:

abracadabra,
just like that,
you've got no rabbit
and you've lost your hat.

As I sneak off home
this familiar refrain
echoes in my head
again and again:

abracadabra,
just like that,
you've got no rabbit
and you've lost your hat.

As I walk through the door,
time after time
my wife and kids
greet me with this rhyme:

abracadbra,
just like that,
you've got no rabbit
and you've lost your hat.

And when I get to heaven
as I hope to do
most probably the angels
will sing along too:

abracadabra,
just like that,
you've got no rabbit
and you've lost your hat.

But when I reach
the celestial throne
perhaps God will show me
a trick of his own,

how, abracadabra,
just like that,
he produced the whole world
out of his hat!

Cuckoo Jones

When he thought he heard
The first cuckoo of Spring,
Said Mr. Jones
"Now there's a thing!"

So he picked up his pen
And wrote to *The Times*,
Just a small letter,
Just a few lines.

But they printed it
As they used to do –
The first *Times* reader
To hear the cuckoo.

That was years ago.
Now he walks down our street
With a shrunken body
And shuffling feet.

Through the skin of his face
You can see the bones,
But we all still love
Mr. Cuckoo Jones.

A Call To Arms

The 4,000-student Bolton Institute of Higher Education... has come up with a cat's collar that emits an ultrasonic sound, which scares not the cat but the birds. At night, when all decent birds are asleep, the collar automatically switches itself off, allowing cats to hunt mice instead. *The Independent* 1.7.99.

We are the birds that fly by night
Beneath the stars and moon.
From crack of dawn we're out of sight
Until late afternoon.
In other words we only wake
For our nocturnal prey
But must we call it God's mistake
That we were made that way?

The decent birds, the sunshine boys,
Have got it safe and sound
And all because the world enjoys
To see them flit around
Whereas we have our work cut out
And we just don't think it's right,
So raise your beaks with us and shout
Indecent birds, unite!

Wordsworth's Watering Can

William Wordsworth named his watering can Kubla after Coleridge's 'Kubla Khan' -
according to George Kirkby, a long-serving guide at Dove Cottage who has recreated
the garden there.

Wordsworth loved his garden,
a small one as gardens go,
just a patch behind Dove Cottage
but beautiful, even so.

And he loved his sister, Dorothy.
They tended the flowers together.
This is the life, they thought,
Oh why can't it last for ever!

So they drenched their dry earth daily
with Kubla whose trusty spout
recalled those measureless caverns
as it fountained the water about.

In the Book of Life it is written:
No greater love hath man
than that he should choose his friend's poem
as the name for a watering-can.

The Sad Story of Terrible Trevor

Terrible Trevor Alucard
Reckoned himself, he said, 'Well Hard'.
His favourite time was after dark.
He stalked the streets, he prowled the park.
"Where are you going?" his Mum would shout
And Trev would always answer "Out!"
At first, it seemed to him enough
To do the usual scary stuff,
Just walk about in studs and leather,
Chains and buckles and whatever
But soon he found this rather boring
Like playing football without scoring.
"What can I do tomorrow night
To give everyone a proper fright?"
He asked himself, then scratched his head
"The trouble with this town - it's dead!"
To tell the truth you'd seldom find
A fresh thought crossing Trevor's mind,
But suddenly he cried out "Hey,
The churchyard's got a right of way
Past all those crosses, angels' wings
And stones and spooky graves and things,
It's just the place to hang around,
To tiptoe up without a sound
And then with a blood-curdling cry
To leap out on any passers-by."
So next day he spent his pocket-money
(All of it, every single penny)
On a cloak and fangs - vampire attire -
From *Van Helsing's Costume Hire*
And took it home. "What's that you've got?"
Asked Trevor's Mum. "I'll tell you what,
Mind your own business woman!" Sad,
But Trev gave answers like his Dad
And just like Dad he snarled and swore

Then stomped upstairs and slammed the door.

So night arrived, and fit to burst,
Trev was ready to do his worst.
I tell you, he could hardly wait
To dress up at the churchyard gate.
Once there he donned his vampire kit,
Just as he'd hoped, a perfect fit.
Now for a passer-by to scare.
As if the answer to a prayer
And much to Trevor's cruel delight
A hurrying figure came in sight.
At first it seemed to be the vicar
Except he was moving rather quicker,
Sort of floating down the path
With a sort of rather nasty laugh
(Crepuscular and melancholy)
Which Trev could tell was far from holy,
And then, alas, – Oh send us grace! –
The two of them met face to face
Like shadows looking in a mirror,
One with a grin, the other terror.
This was now way beyond a joke.
The grin flashed pointed fangs then spoke:

"My, what a silly boy you are,
Pretending to be Dracula
When anyone can see that you
Really haven't got a clue
About blood suction and all that.
You couldn't scare a witch's cat!
Your cloak's too short, your fangs are fake,
Your whole equipment's a mistake,
You should be drinking Seven-Up
Or bedtime cocoa from a cup
Instead of scaring little kids
With talk of garlic, coffin lids

And all the necks you're going to bite.
Still, Trev, since we've met tonight
We might as well become acquainted
(By this time Trev had nearly fainted!)
So shut your eyes and count to ten.
You won't have to pretend again.
Our meeting here is most fortuitous.
I need an apprentice, Trev, and you it is!
You've an awful lot to learn, I know,
But you're keen enough, it seems. Let's go,
Tomorrow is another day
And Transylvania's quite a way!"

With that, a flash and a clap of thunder
A cloak was swirled and Trev tucked under.
He might have given a muffled shout
But there was nobody else about
Except the cold dead, long engraved,
Indifferent to how a boy behaved
And, anyway, far too deep to hear
Or, if they did, too late to care.
Now, in the churchyard, one more stone
Under the yew tree all alone
Says Trevor Alucard RIP
Except he *doesn't*, believe you me!

Once in a Dream

Once in a dream
I gazed at the mirror
and all I could see
was tomorrow forever.

Once in a dream
I started counting
One, two, three
and I couldn't stop.

Once in a dream
the clock ticked backwards
and I watched its hands
going faster and faster.

Once in a dream
snow began falling
and ice grew thick
in the middle of summer.

Once in a dream
I walked through a forest
ignoring the voices
which cried *Go Home!*

Once in a dream
I conquered a mountain
and planted my flag
to say I'd arrived.

Once in a dream
I felt so happy
that I danced through the night
to invisible music.

Once in a dream
I missed a heart-beat
but you were beside me
and took my hand.

Potatoes

One potato two potato
three potato four

sniff them feel them
scrub them peel them
and bounce them on the floor

five potato six potato
seven potato eight

slice them boil them
fry them in oil then
shovel them onto your plate

nine potato ten potato
eleven potato twelve

gobble them swallow them
pudding to follow them
making a pig of yourself

twelve potato eleven potato
ten potato nine

I'll swap you that one
a tit for your tat one
but this potato's mine

eight potato seven potato
six potato five

there's a worm in my gravy
all wriggly and wavy
I think he's still alive

four potato three potato
two potato one

what a horrible dinner
it wasn't a winner
thank goodness it's over and done

Wellington Boots

My Wellington boots, my Wellington boots,
My empty, tempt-me, Wellington boots,
I fill them with slithery tadpoles and newts
And noodles, spaghetti and bamboo shoots
And then I put *on* my Wellington boots.

Everything spills out over the top
With a squelch and slurry, a squirm and a slop
And a horrible gurgle which just won't stop
And I have to clean up the mess with a mop
And Mum says they won't take them back at the shop!

Nothing On Earth

When the sun came out
then went back in again
it was everything you promised
taken away from me
at the point of being given.

I had stood for a moment
in a blaze of happiness
the length of our street
with every door open
to share the good news,

then it clouded over
to be nothing on earth,
like a dried-up river
with the sky on its back
or a door slammed shut.

Song of the Lonely Monster

So many oceans deep,
So many mountains high,
So many slopes so steep,
So many tears to cry.

So many chasms wide,
So many ice-caps cold,
So many hurts inside,
So many griefs to hold.

So many deserts vast,
So many forests drear,
So many ages past
So many more to scare.

So many drifts of snow,
So many stars above,
So many miles to go
And never a friend to love.

At The House of Superstition

There's a crack in the mirror,
An open umbrella,
A table laid for thirteen,
And the grass on the lawn
All shaven and shorn
Is a sinister arsenic green.

There's a ladder that leans
At an angle which means
Pass beneath and there's trouble in store!
And a black cat asleep
And no one to sweep
The salt that lies spilt on the floor.

There's a terminal look
To the Visitor's Book,
No radio, TV or phone.
And today and tomorrow
Are both born to sorrow
Like the magpie which flies off alone.

First Day

Here in this great hall
which smells of polish
the windows are so tall
and the floor so shiny
that everything feels funny
and not right at all
and I wish, I wish

that my sister was here,
that she was next to me,
that she was saying
"Let's watch TV"
but that would be home
and this is school
with everybody waiting

until the music stops
and nobody talking
and me not knowing
anybody, not anybody,
and all of us in lines
with teachers at the front
and sides, not smiling, looking

worried and a bit cross
then one of them
is really friendly
with a big voice saying
Good morning, children
and everybody goes
Good morning, Mrs. Someone

and she has things
to tell us like it's someone's
birthday and I'm feeling
better now, much
better, and I look at the top
of the tallest window
where the sun is shining.

Finding the Magic

You don't have to be a wizard
To find the magic.
This life can be sweet, can be hard,
Can be comic or tragic.

You don't need a beard, a wand
Or a pointy hat
To discover what lies beyond
The everyday matter of fact.

My grandfather could cast a spell
When he told me stories or jokes
And I had a teacher who could as well.
They didn't need spangled cloaks.

What they did was help me to see
How magic lies all around
And that nothing is ordinary,
That we share an uncommon ground.

So, wizards, I tell you this.
For all your special powers,
What's truly magical is
The world that's already ours,

The world in which every day
Is so different, so various,
That whatever your spell books say
It's *you* who have need of *us!*

Another Day on the Beach

If the wind changes
you'll be stuck with that face for ever
and won't it teach you a lesson.
They certainly didn't like my
sour-puss, beetle-browed
I've had enough of this expression.

Oh to get away from it all,
an outgrown sandcastle king
with his bucket and spade regalia.
If I put my mind to it, though,
and dug deep enough
I could manage a smile in Australia.

Fair Exchange

Show me a kitten that doesn't like comfort,
Show me a puppy that won't chase a stick,
Show me rabbit that never eats lettuce,
Show me a tortoise that moves at a lick
And I'll show you a budgie that swoops like an eagle,
I'll show you a goldfish that snaps like a shark,
I'll show you a hamster that thinks its a parrot
And tries to repeat every passing remark.

Who Goes There?

I have no name,
I am not yet born
but I'll wear the clothes
that you have worn.

When you're in trouble
I'll take your side
and there'll be no worries
that you have to hide.

When fear comes knocking
at our door
you won't have to open it
alone any more.

I shall be your brother
but here I stand
in the not-quite-there
of no-man's-land,

so give me the password
without more fuss
and we'll face the world,
just the two of us!

A Cat Understands

When a cat crossed our path
we knew we'd be lucky,
we could tell by its secretive look,
by the way that its tail
stood unusually tall
and the leisurely time that it took.

As it said in cat language
Be loving, be happy
we answered it back in our own,
for a cat understands
that two holding hands
must be better than walking alone.

A Prize Exhibit

"This scatty bouncer is not for beginners."
Warning note on a cage in the rabbit tent
at the Hertfordshire County Show

I'm a flapper, a flouncer,
One of the winners,
But *This scatty bouncer*
Is not for beginners.

I've ears made for stroking
And a soft fur coat.
So you think they're joking?
Believe me, they're not.

If you're after a rabbit
Which does as it's told
And, when you grab it,
Is easy to hold,

A bundle of fluff,
A cuddlesome pet,
Then you're not old enough
To handle me yet.

But if you're scatty
And a bouncer too
I'm the ready, steady
Rabbit for you.

So one for the money,
Two for the show,
Three for the bunny
And go, go, go!

Glove on a Spiked Railing

Rescued, out in the cold,
wearing unfamiliar numbness
like a second skin,
five knitted fingers'
rigid glitter
hadn't abandoned hope
wherever the hand might be
that fitted them

which seemed, that morning,
just how I felt
without you,
stuck there out of touch
as couples passed by
hand in hand,
a solitary gesture
in the name of love
though frozen stiff.

Pet Sounds

Flap rattle, claw scratch,
Purr in a sun patch,
Mad dash, tinkle ball.
Tuna crunch, chitter call,
Bag tear, carpet rip,
Sniff-sneeze at catnip,
Window tap, pane patter,
Oven leap, pan clatter,
Sleep-snuffle, dream-snore
All these, and many more.

The Inner Dog

Here in this city park
I walk the inner dog
which lives with me.

Sometimes his thoughts are dark.
Sometimes he lifts a weary leg
against life's tree.

Sometimes, just for a lark,
he gives his lead a tug
enticingly.

Sometimes I hear him bark
and watch his wide eyes beg
for how things ought to be.

Here in this city park
I walk my inner dog
which nobody can see.

European Eagle Owl at the World Owl Trust

The fierce gun-turret swivel
of a sunk head
bedded in feathers,
the feline preening
of all those downy places
an inquisitive beak discovers,

the angle-poise display of wings
in a loosening shudder
then out to their full length,
the shift, the stretch, the weighing
of airy lightness
against muscular bulk strength.

From the tip of scout-knife ear-tufts
to the scimitar, horned talons
which slice then bloodily withdraw,
here is the indifference
of nature's evolution
and its swift, impartial law.

Learning to be a Ghost

School is just the place for me
to practise after dark,
with no kids in the classrooms
and no cars in the park,
with stillness in the playground,
with silence in the hall,
nothing to distract me,
no one there at all.

Perhaps a little moonlight
spilling on the floor,
perhaps some lurking shadows
along the corridor,
perhaps a not-quite-turned-off tap,
perhaps a broken blind,
but drip-drip-drip and rattle
are sounds I mustn't mind.

So this is where I teach myself
when everyone's gone home,
until I've got the hang of it
I need to be on my own,
but as soon as I'm an expert,
as soon as I've learned to be
a confident and skilful ghost
then you'll be seeing me!

There Was a Time

when I couldn't whistle
or ride a bicycle

or use real money
because I hadn't any

or fit puzzle pieces
or tie my own laces

or even begin
to write with a pen

or choose what to eat
or stay up late

or push a wheely basket
at the supermarket

(instead of sitting on it
like a little puppet)

or reach light switches
or strike matches

or climb the stump of a tree
without getting stuck half-way

or start the alphabet
and reach the end of it.

Of course I can do
all these things now

but I couldn't then,
not one of them.

Songs For Seven Storeys

Songs for Seven Storeys is a cycle of songs written to celebrate the building of the new
Evelina Children's Hospital on London's South Bank. The songs take their subjects from
the seven 'themed' floors of the hospital building which overlooks the gardens of Lambeth
Palace. Set to music by Bob Chilcott, *Songs for Seven Storeys* was performed on 16th and
17th March, 2005, in the hospital atrium and at the Royal Festival Hall, by The City
Chamber Choir with members of the London Philharmonic Orchestra and children from
Little Big Voices, Lambeth Junior Centre for Young Musicians, Streatham Wells Primary
School and Sudbourne Primary School:

PROLOGUE

This is the sound of our lives beginning,
The tap at the shell, the straw-bed rustle,
The bud snapped open, the welcoming,

An overture played on a penny whistle,
A bargain struck by a little tin drum
With time to be patient, with strength to be gentle.

This is the measure of what we become,
The steps of creation joining the dance,
Unsteady at first, to the rock-a-bye tune

Of a nursery rhyme, our inheritance,
The knock at the door, a face in the mirror,
The cry of amazement which grows from a whisper.

OCEAN

Deep as thought
Giving nothing away,
We keep our secrets
From the light of day.

Sun on calm waters
Or wind whipping waves,
What do we care
How the weather behaves?

Ours is the space
You dive to explore,
Aquanaut touchdown
On the ocean floor.

We gape at your cameras,
Dart past your goggles,
A flick of quicksilver,
A flurry of bubbles,

Or a dangerous shadow,
A grin full of teeth
Which doesn't mean laughter
But sudden death.

Then deep in thought
You swim up and away
To ponder our secrets
By the light of day.

ARCTIC

Ours is the glass kingdom where fur and feathers
Are no luxury, where the world's breath
Is a cloud to be lost in, and here they come,
The thermal adventurers padded and packed
With their primus, their pemmican,
Planting their flags, posing for history,
Hugging and cheering but hearing no echo

No echo no echo no echo no echo no echo

While out on the ice we gather or scatter,
Watchful, resourceful, intent on survival
Wherever we are in this all-the-year-round-us
Dazzle of distance. Now see them trudge home
To their armchairs, their firesides
And narrow horizons, leaving us here
In the silence of zero, a world with no echo

No echo no echo no echo no echo no echo no . . .

FOREST

Monkey business, tiger trouble,
Mischief-making at the double,
Monkey babe and tiger cub'll
Join the junior forest club'll
Party until morning.

We like it cool, we like it hot,
We'll give it everything we've got,
We're in the pink, we're on the spot,
We'll show that we know what's what,
You're only young once and then you're not,
Suddenly with no warning!

The old ones in the shade of trees
Who once were tear-aways like these
Will mutter, grumble, groan and wheeze
But all they'll do is scratch their fleas
And go on yawning.

BEACH

We measure time, the sand runs through our fingers.
Here among tarred ropes and rusted anchors
We are the sea-side ghosts returning.

Buckets and spades and castles in the air,
Sandwiches, a rug, a striped deck-chair.
We are the sea-side ghosts returning.

Spray of wet dogs as they bark and shake
And plunge into the waves to chase a stick.
We are the sea-side ghosts returning.

A squelch between the toes, a gritty squeeze,
In search of memories like these
We are the sea-side ghosts returning.

Water withdrawn, the shallow paddle pools,
A treasure trove of little stones and shells.
We are the sea-side ghosts returning.

We measure time, catch happiness in nets,
Show off the prize that each of us collects.
We are the sea-side ghosts returning.

SAVANNAH

Quick slow quick quick slow
A high white light and the dust below

Slow quick slow slow quick
Little dry tongues which dart and flick

Sun-baked savannah, scorched to the bone
Shadowless grass, heat on stone

Necessary patience, heavy tread
Nuzzling the ground with downcast head

Night sky, moonshine, ripple of a breeze
The diamond constellations, the mysteries

Parched earth cools, the healing starts
A fountain of dreams for weary hearts

Solitary traveller, pilgrim band
All of us must pass through this land

The bear looked over the mountain
To see what he could see
The bear looked over the mountain
And all that he could see
Was a valley full of sunlight
And a river running free.

The bear looked over the mountain
To see what he could see
The bear looked over the mountain
And all that he could see
Was a picture of his heart's content
Where he would like to be.

The bear looked over the mountain
To see what he could see
The bear looked over the mountain
And all that he could see
Was sunlight on the river
And fruit on every tree.

The bear looked over the mountain
To see what he could see
The bear look over the mountain
And all that he could see
Just made him say over and over
That's the place for me!

EPILOGUE (SKY)

The silver speck, the vapour trail, a message
Loop the looping on the blue: We are leaving you
But get well soon. We have booked your passage

And wait for you to join us. Up here are no
Vain regrets, no looking down or back
To yesterday. Wherever we go

Will be your future too. We wish you luck
As the clouds go rolling by. Remember this song
When you follow us, when the journey you make

Starts out. Soon you'll be flying home
To the welcome we promised. Over and done
And a new beginning already begun.